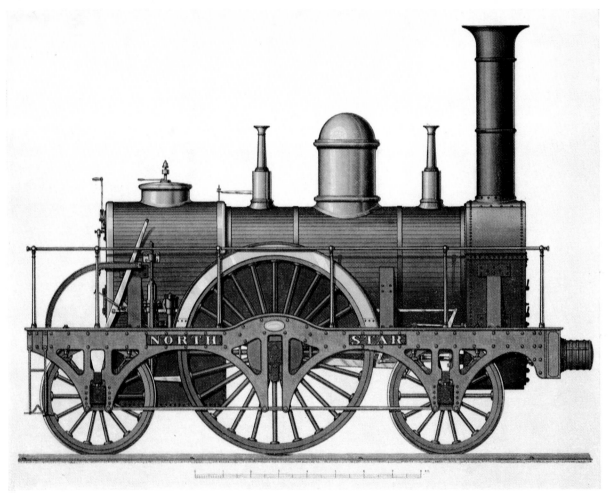

Stephenson's 2–2–2 *North Star* Locomotive: Great Western Railway, 1837

SCIENCE MUSEUM

The British Railway Locomotive

A BRIEF PICTORIAL HISTORY OF THE FIRST FIFTY YEARS
OF THE BRITISH STEAM RAILWAY LOCOMOTIVE

1803-1853

COMPILED BY G. F. WESTCOTT

LONDON: HER MAJESTY'S STATIONERY OFFICE
1958

The front cover picture shows
Trevithick's 2–2–0 London locomotive
Catch me who can, 1808

The picture opposite shows
the *Novelty* locomotive, 1829, and train,
from an early lithograph by R. Martin

SBN 11 290152 2

Printed in England for HER MAJESTY'S STATIONERY OFFICE
by Headley Brothers Ltd 109 Kingsway London WC2 and Ashford Kent
Dd.503873. K.72

RAILWAYS, worked by horses, would appear to have been introduced into England before the middle of the seventeenth century and were developed particularly in the coal-mining districts of Newcastle and Durham. Early in the following century cast iron came into use instead of wood for wagon wheels and for the wearing surfaces of the rails, and, later, rails were made entirely of cast iron. In 1750 M. Menzies patented the self-acting plane for railways—that is the use of descending loaded wagons to draw up empty wagons— though the system does not appear to have been used for surface railways until near the end of the century, while the first application of a steam winding engine to draw loaded wagons up an inclined railway appears to have been made about 1805.

Early Experiments, 1797–1808

Early atmospheric steam engines were far too heavy and bulky for their successful application to locomotives, but attempts to develop high-pressure steam road locomotives were made towards the end of the eighteenth century. About 1797 R. Trevithick made three models, one of which had four wheels and may have represented a suggestion for a railway locomotive. A sketch, dated 1803, shows a design for a Trevithick railway engine (Plate 1), probably intended to run on the tramway at the Coalbrookdale Iron Works, but unfortunately, there is no conclusive evidence that the engine was ever run with a test load. A Trevithick engine certainly ran on the Pen-y-darran line in 1804, and it is conjectured that its design may have been based on that shown in the 1803 sketch. Later, improved Trevithick engines were made, in 1805 (Plate 2), and 1808 (Front cover). It is possible that breakages of the rails due to the weight of the engines were the main cause of the failure of these experiments.

The Colliery Locomotive, 1812–1825

The first practically successful railway locomotive was J. Blenkinsop's rack locomotive of 1812 (Plate 3). It ran on strong cast iron edge rails and adhesion was secured by the rack. The original arrangement of the engine is uncertain, but it was soon changed to two double-acting cylinders with cranks at right angles, so as to ensure a start from any position.

After experiments to prove that smooth wheels running on smooth rails would provide adequate traction, W. Hedley built *Puffing Billy* (Plate 4 shows the type) in 1813. It was first mounted on four wheels, but breakages of the cast-iron plate rails resulted in eight wheels being used from 1815 to 1830, when the relaying of the line with wrought-iron edge rails enabled a return to four wheels to be made.

George Stephenson built his first locomotive in 1814. Its design is unknown, but it has been suggested that it was on the lines of Blenkinsop's engine without the rack. In 1815 Stephenson made the first of his *Killingworth* engines. After trying internal cranks to connect the driving wheels, he adopted a chain and sprockets (Plate 5). The use of pistons pressed downwards on the axles by the boiler pressure helped to ensure a better distribution of the load on the wheels and track. Steam was distributed by slide valves and the use of loose eccentrics enabled the engines to be reversed.

J. Birkinshaw's patent for fish-bellied rolled-iron edge rails, 1829, marks the practical introduction of rails of this much stronger and tougher material which enabled heavier locomotives to be used. After experiments, parallel wrought-iron rails were adopted for the London and Birmingham Railway opened in 1837–8.

In 1823 the firm of Robert Stephenson and Company was formed mainly for the purpose of building locomotives and Robert took over from his father the main responsibility for engine development. Among its earliest products was *Locomotion* (Plate 6) for the Stockton and Darlington Railway, built in 1825, and the first locomotive for a public railway. *Locomotion* had outside coupling rods.

The Vindication of Steam, 1827–1829

It soon became doubtful whether steam could compete economically with horse traction on the Darlington Railway, but T. Hacksworth's powerful six-coupled engine, *Royal George* (Plate 7), built in 1827, successfully established the superiority of steam.

The Stephenson locomotive was now being developed rapidly and experimentally, the main object being to increase the power while reducing the weight and spreading it more equally on the rails so as to reduce rail breakages. The *Lancashire Witch* (Plate 8), marked an important advance, since its inclined outside cylinders enabled all its axles to be sprung. The use of a boiler with two furnace tubes shows that boiler development was also receiving attention.

When the Liverpool and Manchester Railways was considering what kind of traction should be used on its line, it was decided to promote a trial of locomotives. Among the interesting locomotives entered was Braithwaite and Ericsson's *Novelty* (Plate 9), which had a boiler with a long single firetube and vertical cylinders driving through bell-cranks. It had no tender and might be regarded as a tank locomotive as it carried a small water tank on the engine frame.

The outstanding engine at the Rainhill Trials, held in October 1829, was, however, the first prize winner, Stephenson's *Rocket* (Plate 10), which alone complied with all the stipulated conditions. Its success was mainly due to its use of the multiple firetube boiler in place of the single flue boilers previously used. By this means the boiler heating surface and the production of steam were enormously increased and, consequently, the power of a steam locomotive of a given weight was augmented so greatly that, at one bound, steam locomotives' speeds were raised from about those of a carthorse to more than those of the fastest racehorse. The success of the *Rocket* was perhaps the most important single event in railway history.

The use of coke as fuel was compulsory at the Rainhill Trials, and its use was continued on public passenger railways until after the middle of the century.

Locomotive Design Improves, 1830–1834

Following the *Rocket* locomotive, development was very rapid. The *Rocket* had no smokebox, an external firebox and rather steeply inclined outside cylinders, while the *Northumbrian* (Plate 11), built in 1830, had a smokebox, an internal firebox and nearly horizontal cylinders. Later in the same year the *Planet* (Plate 12) combined the smokebox with the internal firebox, single central blast pipe and horizontal cylinders at the front end of the boiler—features which have been found on almost all steam railway locomotives since built. Following the *Planet*, the sandwich frame, of wood between two thin iron plates, was developed and was much used for many years, notably on the Great Western Railway broad gauge. The slide valves were placed above the cylinders and operated through rockers. For goods services four-coupled *Planet* type engines were generally used (Plate 13).

One of the most interesting varieties of the *Planet* type is shown by G. Forrester and Company's *Vauxhall* (Plate 14), built in 1834 for the Dublin and Kingstown Railway, the first steam railway in Ireland. The engine had outside, instead of inside, cylinders, and a double outside plate frame in place of an outside sandwich frame.

In 1832 two of the four-coupled *Planet* type locomotives of the Leicester and Swannington Railway, opened that year, were fitted with additional trailing axles behind the firebox, thus giving them the 0–4–2 wheel arrangement. It was found that the added axle not only helped to spread the load, making heavier and more powerful locomotives possible, but also improved the steadiness of the engine when running. Thus the six-wheeled engine with 'locomotive-type' boiler was introduced (Plate 15). The first 2–2–2 locomotive was the *Patentee*, built for the Liverpool and Manchester Railway in 1833, and the last 2–2–2 to run regularly in England was G.W.R. No. 165, withdrawn in December 1912. The 0–6–0 engine (Plate 16), which was later to become the commonest type of goods engine in this country and is still in use today, appeared in 1834, though for several years Stephenson's standard goods engines were of the 2–4–0 type.

The Railway System Grows, 1836–1842

New railways were now being built all over Britain. In 1836 the opening of the London and Greenwich Railway brought the first passenger locomotive to London. In 1838 the partial opening of the Great Western broad gauge railway released a number of freak locomotive designs, among which Stephenson engines, and particularly the *North Star* (Frontispiece), shone as examples of sanity. D. Gooch, when designing his famous standard passenger engines introduced in 1840, is said to have taken the *North Star* as his basis. On the London and Birmingham Railway, opened in 1837–8, E. Bury & Company's engines were at first used exclusively. This firm was probably the most powerful rival to the Stephensons of the increasing number of locomotive manufacturers now appearing on the scene. Bury engines were very distinctive (Plate 17), with their inside bar frames and high copper-domed fireboxes of D-shape in plan. Although by this time six-wheeled locomotives were generally used (Plate 18), Bury continued to make only four-wheelers for several more years. During 1838 to 1842 a number of bogie singles (Plate 19), designed by the American W. Norris, were made for use on the Birmingham and Gloucester Railway, some being imported from America.

Locomotive Improvements, 1839–1841

In early locomotives the boilers and frames were rigidly connected, so that when the boiler expanded, heat stresses and distortions were set up in the frames and working parts with detrimental results. In 1839 I. Dodds, on the Sheffield and Rotherham Railway, fixed his boilers to the frame at the front end only, allowing the firebox end to slide on the frame. About the middle of the century this practice was widely used.

In 1841 R. Stephenson patented the 'long boiler' locomotive, in which all three carrying axles were placed in the space between the smokebox and firebox. The main object was to use longer firetubes to extract more heat, and hence increase the efficiency of the boiler, without increasing the wheelbase. Other important features of the patent where the use of slide valves on their sides in a central common valve chest driven directly without rocking shafts and the adoption of single inside plate frames: the former feature soon became common and the latter, eventually, universal in Britain. Since the *Planet*, Stephenson had nearly always used a sandwich outside frame with several inner frames joining the firebox to the smokebox, one of the objects being to give additional support to the crankshaft, and this change may indicate that crankshafts could now be relied on for strength. The single inside frame provided a more direct means of distributing the stresses between the cylinders and crankshaft, the boiler, the wheels and the buffer beams. Bury, as already mentioned, had previously used single inside bar frames. The earliest inside single plate frames were welded and the horn plates were usually bolted on. As will be seen, however, outside frames continued to be used, and engines with such frames were built as late as the early part of the present century. While outside frames added to the weight and cost of a locomotive, some engineers thought that a much steadier engine requiring less maintenance resulted.

Valve Gear Developments, 1835–1840

Meanwhile, important developments were taking place in the design of valve gears. In 1835 Stephenson engines began to be fitted with Carmichael's two-eccentric forked gab valve gears, invented in 1818, which eliminated the need for hand valve levers, while in 1836 the Stephenson company adopted four-eccentric gab gears, though these had been used previously by other makers.

Early locomotive slide valves were practically without lap, only enough being provided to ensure that steam could not enter both ends of the cylinder simultaneously, sufficient angular lead being given to enable steam to reach the piston at the beginning of its power stroke. Consequently boiler pressure acted on the piston almost to the end of its stroke, while the opening to exhaust was so late that there was considerable back pressure due to the steam being partially trapped. The four-eccentric valve gear gave an easy means of experiment, and in 1838 the *Lightning* on the Liverpool and Manchester Railways was fitted with slide valves having their outside laps increased from $\frac{1}{8}$ in. to $\frac{3}{8}$ in., increasing the angular advance to suit. This caused the exhaust port to open earlier, thus greatly easing the back pressure, and 25 per cent reduction in fuel consumption, with higher speeds, was obtained. In 1840 J. Dewrance fitted the *Rapid* with valves having outside laps of 1 in. with $4\frac{1}{2}$ in. travel. This gave cut-off at 79 per cent and exhaust at 95 per cent of the stroke.

The importance of the correct timing of valve events (admission, cut-off, release and compression) and the advantages of expansive working were becoming realised. In 1840 J. Gray's 2–2–2 engines for the Hull and Selby Railway used his complicated and rather unpractical variable expansion gear with the then high boiler pressure of 90 lb. per sq. in. Another interesting feature of these engines was their mixed frames with inside bearings for the driving axles and outside bearings for the carrying axles.

2*

The Link Valve Gear, 1841–1842

About 1841 W. Williams suggested connecting the forward and reverse eccentrics by means of a slotted link containing a sliding block from which motion was transmitted to the slide valve. This suggestion was put into practical form by W. Howe in 1842 and applied by Stephenson to a goods locomotive on October 15th in the same year, and so the gear is generally known as Stephenson's link motion. The general effect of 'linking up', that is, moving the reversing lever towards its central position, was to make all the valve events, such as cut-off, release, compression and admission, occur earlier in the cycle. Engines with this gear retained the full power needed for starting and low-speed climbing of earlier engines but by 'linking up' were also able to run much more economically and smoothly at high speeds without overtaxing the boiler. (Very roughly, under easy conditions, normal sustained express train speeds increased from nearly thirty to nearly fifty miles per hour.) By the middle of the century, the design of link valve gears was well understood and attention had also been given to 'streamlining' and enlarging the steam and, especially, the exhaust passages and to the design of the blast pipe. With increased expansive working boiler pressures rose rapidly.

Some Interesting Locomotives, 1843–1853

'Long boiler' engines were used in considerable numbers for several years in Britain; and were even more popular on the Continent. The design did result in a saving of fuel. The 0–6–0 goods (Plate 20), introduced in 1843, was probably the most satisfactory type and continued to be built until 1860, while of the passenger designs, Stephenson's 'A' type with (2–2)–2–0 wheel arrangement (Plate 21), made from 1845 to 1849, was perhaps the best. By placing the outside cylinder between the leading wheels, and thus near the centre of the engine, the tendency to 'yaw', which was a defect in most 'long boiler' locomotives, was reduced.

In 1845 Allan's engines with mixed frames and outside cylinders (Plate 22), which are said to have been designed to avoid the frequent breakages of inside crankshafts on sharp curves, made their first appearance. Sharp's characteristic outside frame 'singles' (Plate 23) had been well known since 1837. Wilson's famous *Jenny Lind* type locomotives (Plate 24) were first built in 1847. *Jenny Linds*, though comparatively small, were very lively and could compete with larger engines because of the excellence of their design and the high boiler pressure used. At this time, 1847, the Great Western Railway were producing many fine engines for the broad gauge, such as the six-coupled goods (Plate 25), and the 'single' (Plate 26), both with inside sandwich frames, and the famous eight-wheelers (Plate 27), which were to remain almost unchanged in essential design until the end of the broad gauge in 1892.

In 1843 T. R. Crampton patented his engine with the driving axle behind the firebox, the object being to enable large driving wheels to be used while keeping the centre of gravity low. The most famous of the *Cramptons* was the eight-wheeled *Liverpool* built in 1848 (Plate 28).

In 1848 the Kitson firm made the first six-coupled goods engines which combined trailing axles behind the fireboxes with inside plate frames and inside cylinders, but the boilers were not free to expand, since the firebox sides were incorporated in the frames.

Tank engines came into practical use about 1837 when two Forrester well tanks were made for the Dublin and Kingstown Railway. The first side tank locomotives were built by C. Tayleur & Co. in 1846, while in 1849 Gooch introduced bogies on the Great Western Railway in his 4–4–0 saddle tanks (Plate 29).

By the middle of the century four-coupled passenger engines were sometimes used (Plate 30), though 'singles' remained the standard for normal main line service. J. E. McConnell's *Bloomers*, 1851, were among the best of the early 2–2–2 i.c. engines, other than 'long boilers', to have inside plate frames. These frames extended the full length of the engine from the front buffer beam and passed outside the firebox.

The series of pictures ends with Stephenson's 2–2–2 engine for the Midland Railway, built in 1852, (Plate 31), and J. Pearson's remarkable double-bogie express tank locomotive (Plate 32), built for the Bristol and Exeter broad gauge line in 1853.

Locomotives and Rails, 1825–1854

Allowable axles loads, and hence locomotive weights, depend largely on rail strength. For example, the wrought-iron fish-bellied rails on the Liverpool and Manchester Railway in 1830 weighed 35 lb. per yard while a parallel double-head rail used on the Midland Railway in 1850 weighed 80 lb. per yard.

The table at the foot of facing page, detailing particulars

of standard gauge goods engines, gives a good indication of locomotive development from 1825 to 1854.

Locomotive Accessories and Details, 1803–1854

Accessories are useful clues for dating locomotives.

D. Papin's lever weight-loaded safety-valve (1681) was used in locomotive boilers until Hackworth introduced his direct spring-loaded valve in 1827 (Plate 7). This was soon followed by the lever spring-balance valve (Plate 11) which enabled the driver to estimate boiler pressure by the 'feel' of the lever, until the coming of the Bourdon pressure gauge (1849).

Plaited spun-yarn formed the piston packing of *Locomotion* in 1825, while the *Rocket* in 1829 had split metal rings pressed against the cylinder walls by internal springs. J. Ramsbottom patented his self-sprung split rings in 1852.

Glass water gauges, used by J. Watt on stationary boilers in 1776, supplemented test cocks on the *Rocket*.

Boiler feed pumps were nearly always driven off the engine motion and for a time, especially on the Great Western Railway, were supplemented by hand pumps. From 1848 steam donkey pumps were sometimes used.

Steam domes and safety-valve covers were sometimes used from 1829 (Plate 10), and frame stays in 1831 (Plate 13). Brakes were first fitted on a tender in 1831, but rarely on locomotives, except tank engines, until about the last quarter of the nineteenth century. In 1833 steam whistles appeared and brass began to replace copper for firetubes.

About 1835 the rotary disc valve regulator replaced plug valves. The slide valve gridiron regulator appeared in 1841, but was not much used for several years, while the double slide-valve regulator seems to have been first used by Crampton about 1848.

Rail guards came into use about 1837 (Plate 17).

Bury's domed 'haystack' fireboxes appeared in 1831 and, between 1840 and 1848, Stephenson and some other makers made many 'Gothic' high fireboxes (Plates 20 and 26).

Balance weights on the driving wheels were introduced in 1840, but their use spread slowly (Plates 26, 27 and 31).

Date	Name	Type	Weight (tons)	Wheel Base ft.	in.	Heating Surface (sq. ft.)	Cylinder Size (in.)	Boiler Pressure (lb./sq. in.)
1825	*Locomotion*	0-4-0	About 7	5	2	60	10×24	50
1827	*Royal George*	0-6-0	About 8·4	8	6	141	11×20	50
1831	*Samson*	0-4-0	10	4	9	457	14×16	50
1834	*Atlas*	0-6-0	17	11	$7\frac{1}{2}$	$651\frac{1}{2}$	16×20	50
1845	*Hector*	0-6-0	Probably about $22\frac{1}{2}$	11 (long boiler)	3	874	15×24	Probably about 80
1843	*McConnel goods*	0-6-0	26·6	15	0	1309	16×24	150

Cast-iron wheels were used at first, with, from 1821, wrought-iron tyres. Later a great variety of constructions appeared for engine wheels, using cast iron, wrought iron and sometimes wood. Solid wrought-iron wheels were commonly employed from 1847 onwards. From about 1834 to 1854 the middle wheels of six-wheeled Stephenson locomotives were generally flangeless. A few other makers also followed this practice (Plates 16, 18, 31 and 32).

About 1840, sandboxes appear on the sides of some engines (Plate 20). These were fitted with outlet valves controlled from the footplate from 1847 (Plates 23 and 24).

Though spring buffers were first fitted in 1834 (Plate 14), stuffed leather buffers usually appeared in front of engines until the middle of the century (Plates 30, 31 and 32).

Some General Considerations

At first there were no special liveries for locomotives, and on the Liverpool and Manchester Railway, for example, the engines were originally painted in a wide variety of different colours, but before the middle of the century the larger railway companies appear to have adopted more or less standard colour schemes. Perhaps the change was partly due to the fact that railways at first bought their engines mainly from private manufacturers, whereas later they built many of their own locomotives. Hackworth built the *Royal George* in 1827 at the railway company's work at Shildon, and later other engines also. The first large railway works was inaugurated in 1843 at Crewe for the Grand Junction Railway. Swindon Works built its first locomotive for the Great Western Railway in 1846.

Railway working conditions are so varied that a wide range of different types of locomotives is essential. By 1853 many unsuitable designs had been eliminated by practical experience and a number of successful types had been developed to satisfy the moderate needs of the time. A locomotive must be highly adaptable, and hence a compromise in design. While science and invention have made important contributions to the development of particular parts of steam locomotives, probably the most important factors have been the experience and the intuitive judgment of those engineers who have evolved the best combination of parts to suit the vagaries of the particular services for which their engines were intended.

DESCRIPTIONS OF PLATES

(*Front cover*) Trevithick's 2–2–0 London locomotive, *Catch me who can*, 1808

Based on an original engraved card. A single vertical cylinder directly drove both rear wheels by return connecting rods. Cast-iron boiler. Weight 8 tons. Said to have reached 12 m.p.h.

(*Frontispiece*) Stephenson's 2–2–2 *North Star* locomotive: Great Western Railway, 1837

Museum drawing based on original Stephenson's working drawings and a sketch by E. T. Lane made about 1848. This broad gauge engine had 16 in. by 16 in. cylinders. Wheelbase

12·33 ft. Heating surface 644·6 sq. ft. Weight *c.* 18·5 tons. Steam pressure 50 to 60 lb. per sq. in. Four-eccentric forked gab valve gear.

PLATE 1. Trevithick's Coalbrookdale locomotive, 1803

Museum drawing based on an original contemporary sketch. A single horizontal cylinder, 4·75 in. by 36 in., enclosed in a cast-iron return-flue boiler and provided with a flywheel, drove the wheels on one side only through spur gears. Steam was distributed through plug valves worked by tappets. Cylinder placed at same end of boiler as furnace door. Boiler pressure *c.* 50 lb. per sq. in. Cast-iron plate rails. Axles mounted directly on boiler, without a separate frame. No flanges on wheels.

PLATE 2. Trevithick's 0–4–0 Newcastle locomotive, 1805

From an original contemporary drawing. A single horizontal cylinder, 9 in. by 36 in., with flywheel, drove both axles by gearing. Cylinder placed at opposite end of boiler to furnace door. Probably the first railway locomotive with flanged wheels. The rails were of wood and probably too weak. No separate frame. A water tank appears to have been fitted under the boiler. Plug and tappet valve gear. Flanged wheels.

PLATE 3. Blenkinsop's rack locomotive, 1812

Museum drawing based mainly on contemporary prints and descriptions. Two vertical cylinders, 9 in. by 22 in., driving separate cranks at right angles were geared to the rack wheel which worked in a rack cast on the edge rails on one side only of the track. The carrying wheels were not driven. Plug valves driven by fixed eccentrics. Reversing by turning plugs through 90 degrees. Cast-iron boiler. Weight about 5 tons. Inside wooden frame carried a small water tank. Flanged wheels.

PLATE 4. Hedley's 0–8–0 locomotive for Wylam, 1813–14

From an engraving in Wood's *A Practical Treatise on Railroads*, 1825. Three similar engines were made. One, *Puffing Billy*, had two vertical cylinders, 9 in. by 36 in., one on each side of the boiler and partly enclosed in it, and drove a single crankshaft coupled to the wheels by spur gearing. Wrought-iron return flue boiler having 77 sq. ft. heating surface and working at 50 lb. per sq. in. Weight 8·3 tons. Slide valves worked by tappets. Separate inside wooden frames and tender for fuel and water.

PLATE 5. Stephenson's 0–4–0 Killingworth locomotive, *c.* 1815

From an original water-colour, possibly made by George Stephenson. Two vertical cylinders, 9 in. by 24 in., enclosed in the single-flue wrought-iron boiler. Each cylinder drove one axle by return connecting rods, the axles being coupled by a chain. Heating surface *c.* 80 sq. ft. Weight *c.* 6 tons. Steam pressure 50 lb. per sq. in. Wheel base 7·17 ft. Slide valves were driven by loose eccentrics, so as to give reverse. Inside horizontal plate frame. Flanged wheels.

PLATE 6. Stephenson's 0–4–0 *Locomotion* for the Stockton and Darlington Railway, 1825

Museum drawing based mainly on contemporary illustrations and descriptions and the existing remains. Two vertical cylinders, 9·5 in. by 24 in., enclosed in single-flue boiler. Each cylinder drove one of the axles which were connected by outside coupling rods. Heating surface *c.* 60 sq. ft. Weight *c.* 7 tons. Wheel base 5·17 ft. No separate frame. Loose eccentric valve gear.

PLATE 7. Hackworth's 0–6–0 *Royal George* locomotive, Stockton and Darlington Railway, 1827

Museum drawing based mainly on contemporary drawings and descriptions. Two inverted vertical cylinders, 11 in. by 20 in., one on each side of and outside the return-flue boiler, drove the same axle directly. The other two axles were mounted on springs and connected to the driving axle by outside coupling rods. Single blast pipe. Weight *c.* 8·4 tons. Heating surface 141 sq. ft. Wheel base 8 ft. 6 in. Inside horizontal plate frame. Loose eccentric valve gear. Direct loaded spring safety-valve.

Plate 8. Stephenson's 0–4–0 *Lancashire Witch* locomotive, 1828

From plates in *Annales des Mines*, Tome VI, 1829. Two inclined outside cylinders, 9 in. by 24 in., at the firebox end of the boiler, drove the front wheels. The boiler had two single flues and had a heating surface of 66 sq. ft. Wheelbase 5 ft. Weight 7 tons. A wooden inside frame was used and both axles were mounted on springs. Loose eccentric valve gear.

Plate 9. Braithwaite and Ericsson's 0–2–2 *Novelty* well-tank locomotive, 1829

From a lithograph by R. Martin. Two vertical cylinders, 6 in. by 12 in., drove one axle, through bell-cranks and an inside crankshaft. The boiler had a vertical firebox and a horizontal barrel containing a single tube 31 ft. long which reversed its direction twice before reaching the funnel. Boiler pressure, 50 lb. per sq. in. Heating surface was about 42·5 sq. ft. The engine weighed 3·85 tons. Wheelbase 6 ft. Both axles mounted on springs. Bellows provided the draught. Inside wooden frame. Two fixed eccentrics and gab valve gear for reversing.

Plate 10. Stephenson's *Rocket* 0–2–2 o.c. locomotive, Liverpool and Manchester Railway, 1829

Museum drawing based on remains and contemporary illustrations and descriptions. Two outside inclined cylinders, 8 in. by 16·5 in., drove the front axle. The cylindrical boiler had 25 copper firetubes, an external copper firebox and no smokebox. The steam was exhausted into two contracted jets opening upwards near the bottom of the chimney. Boiler pressure *c.* 50 lb. per sq. in. Heating surface 138 sq. ft. Both axles sprung. Weight 4·25 tons. Wheelbase 4 ft. Inside horizontal plate and bar frame. Loose eccentric valve gear with fixing mechanism.

Plate 11. Stephenson's *Northumbrian* 0–2–2 o.c. locomotive Liverpool and Manchester Railway, 1830

From an engraving by I. Shaw, 1831. Generally similar to the *Rocket*, but the cylinders, 11 in. by 16 in., were nearly horizontal and the boiler had an internal firebox and a smokebox. Heating surface 411·75 sq. ft. Weight 7·3 tons. Wheelbase 7·5 ft. The main frames were formed of vertical plates to which the axle-box horns were bolted.

Plate 12. Stephenson's *Planet* 2–2–0 i.c. locomotive, Liverpool and Manchester Railway, 1830

From a contemporary lithograph by H. Austen. The boiler was similar to the *Northumbrian* and had a heating surface of 408 sq. ft. The cylinders, 11 in. by 16 in., were placed horizontally below the smokebox and drove the back axle. A central single contracted blast pipe in the smokebox opened near the bottom of the funnel. Boiler pressure 50 lb. per sq. in. Weight 8 tons. Wheelbase 5 ft. 2 in. Outside wooden frame strengthened in places by metal plates. From this the sandwich frame was developed.

Plate 13. Stephenson's *George Stephenson* 0–4–0 i.c. locomotive, Glasgow and Garnkirk Railway, 1831

From a woodcut in D. O. Hill's *Views of the Glasgow and Garnkirk Railway*, 1832. The engine was of the *Samson*, or four-coupled *Planet*, type used for goods trains. The cylinders, 11 in. by 16 in., drove the back axle and were slightly inclined so that the piston rod worked below the leading axle. Heating surface 319·17 sq. ft. Pressure 50 lb. per sq. in. Weight said to be 6½ tons, empty. Outside sandwich frame.

Plate 14. Forrester's *Vauxhall* 2–2–0 o.c. locomotive, Dublin and Kingstown Railway, 1834

Museum drawing based on Plate VI, Fig. 5, in Deghilage's *Origine de la Locomotive*, 1886 and other sources. Horizontal outside cylinders, 11 in. by 18 in., with vibrating pillar parallel motion. Said to have had four-eccentric gab valve gear. Double outside plate frame. Weight 11 tons.

PLATE 15. Stephenson's 0–4–2 i.c. goods locomotive, Stanhope and Tyne Railway, c. 1834

From a lithograph in F. W. Simms' *Public Works of Great Britain*, 1838. Probably one of the three built for this line in 1834. These had 14 in. by 18 in. cylinders. Heating surface *c.* 420 sq. ft. Outside sandwich frame. Loose eccentric valve gear.

PLATE 16. Tayleur's 0–6–0 i.c. locomotive, Leicester and Swannington Railway, 1835

Museum drawing based on an original Tayleur working drawing. Cylinders 16 in. by 20 in. Heating surface, 651·4 sq. ft. Weight 17 tons. Wheelbase 11 ft. 7½ in. Outside sandwich frame. Loose eccentric valve gear.

PLATE 17. Bury's 2–2–0 i.c. locomotive, London and Birmingham Railway, 1837–39

Based on tracings from original Bury working drawings and contemporary illustrations. The dimensions of wheels and wheelbase do not agree with any particular engine on the L. & B. R., but the design is like those of Bury's early engines. Cylinders probably 12 or 13 in. by 18 in. Weight *c.* 10 tons. Wheelbase 6 ft. 5 in. Heating surface *c.* 463 sq. ft. Four eccentric valve gear.

PLATE 18. Stephenson's 2–2–2 i.c. standard passenger engine, 1838

From an engraving in J. Weale's *Description of the Patent Locomotive Steam Engine*, 1838. Cylinders 12 in. by 18 in. Boiler pressure 50 lb. per sq. in. Wheelbase 9 ft. 2 in. Four eccentric valve gear.

PLATE 19. Norris' 4–2–0 o.c. locomotive, probably Birmingham and Gloucester Railway, 1839–42.

From an original water-colour by E. T. Lane, dated 29.6.1849. An American-designed engine, with front bogie and bar frame. The B. & G. R. had forty of these made between 1838 and 1840, and the example shown was probably built by the Nasmyth firm in England. Cylinders probably 11½ in. by 20 in. Boiler pressure *c.* 55 lb. per sq. in. Wheelbase 9 ft. 6 in. Four eccentric valve gear.

PLATE 20. Kitson's 0–6–0 i.c. *Hector* 'long boiler' locomotive, York and North Midland Railway, 1845

Museum drawing based on original Kitson working drawings. Cylinders 15 in. by 24 in. Heating surface 874 sq. ft. Wheelbase 11 ft. 3 in. Weight probably *c.* 22 tons. Stephenson's link valve gear. Inside plate frame with horn plates bolted on. Boiler pressure probably *c.* 80 lb. per sq. in.

PLATE 21. Stephenson's 'A' type (2–2)–2–0 o.c. 'long boiler' locomotive, London and North Western Railway (S. Division), 1846–47

Museum drawing based on original Stephenson working drawings and other early sources. Cylinders 15 in. by 24 in. Wheelbase 13 ft. Boiler heating surface 830 sq. ft. The largest engines of this type on the L.N.W.R. had 939·4 sq. ft. heating surface and weighed 24·2 tons.

PLATE 22. Allan's 2–2–2 o.c. *Velocipede* passenger locomotive (No. 187), London and North Western Railway (N. Division), 1847

From an original water-colour by A. Allan. This illustration shows an Allan design with 7-ft. driving wheels. Notice also the use of large outside eccentrics. Cylinders 15 in. by 20 in. Wheelbase *c.* 13 ft. Mixed frame. Weight *c.* 19½ tons. Heating surface *c.* 700 sq. ft. 120 lb. per sq. in. Only one engine of this experimental form was made, though many other similar engines were built with 6 ft. and 7 ft. driving wheels.

PLATE 23. Sharp's 2–2–2 i.c. locomotive, 1847

From a contemporary engraving. This represents a standard Sharp 'single' of the period. The typical outside sandwich frame and boiler fittings will be noticed.

PLATE 24. Wilson's 2–2–2 i.c. *Jenny Lind* locomotive, 1847

Based on prints of drawings published in *Practical Mechanics*, 1848. Cylinders 15 in. by 20 in. Heating surface 800 sq. ft. Wheelbase 13 ft. 6 in. Pressure 120 lb. per sq. in. Mixed frame. Typical Wilson boiler fittings.

PLATE 25. Gooch's 0–6–0 i.c. *Pyracmon* locomotive, Great Western Railway, 1847

From an early water-colour. A broad gauge design with 16 in. by 24 in. cylinders and inside sandwich frame. Weight 27½ tons. Wheelbase 15 ft. 5 in. Boiler pressure 115 lb. per sq. in. and heating surface 1373 sq. ft. *Pyracmon* or *Alligator* class. Gooch's, or stationary link, valve gear.

PLATE 26. Gooch's 2–2–2 i.c. *Queen* locomotive, Great Western Railway, 1847

From a water colour by E. T. Lane, dated July 3rd, 1849. Broad gauge engine with inside sandwich frame. Cylinders 16 in. by 24 in. Boiler pressure *c.* 100 lb. per sq. in. Heating surface 1081 sq. ft. Weight *c.* 26·2 tons. Wheelbase 14 ft. 10 in. *Prince* class engine.

PLATE 27. Gooch's (2–2)–2–2 i.c. *Iron Duke* locomotive, Great Western Railway, 1847

From an engraving in Tredgold's *The Steam Engine*, Part 1, Plate I, 1851. Broad gauge engine with outside sandwich frame. Cylinders 18 in. by 24 in. Boiler pressure originally 100 lb. per sq. in.; later increased to 115 lb. per sq. in. Heating surface 1944·8 sq. ft. Weight 35½ tons. Wheelbase 15 ft. 6 in. Gooch's valve gear. *Iron Duke* class engine.

PLATE 28. Bury's (2–2–2)–2–0 o.c. *Liverpool* locomotive, London and North Western Railway, 1848

From a water-colour by E. T. Lane, dated Sept. 20th, 1849. Cylinders 18 in. by 24 in. Boiler heating surface 2290 sq. ft. Steam pressure 120 lb. per sq. in. Wheelbase 18 ft. 5¾ in. Weight 35 tons. Stephenson link motion. Mixed frame.

PLATE 29. Gooch's 4–4–0 i.c. *Corsair* saddle tank locomotive, Great Western Railway, 1849

Plate VII from D. K. Clark's *Railway Machinery*, 1855. Broad gauge engine. Cylinders 17 in. by 24 in. Wheelbase 18 ft. 2 in. Weight 35¾ tons. Inside frames. Gooch's link motion. *Bogie* class engine. Skid rail brake.

PLATE 30. Hawthorn's 2–4–0 i.c. locomotive (No. 2), Oxford, Wolverhampton and Worcester Railway, 1852

From a water-colour by D. Joy, dated August 1858. Cylinders 16 in. by 20 in. Boiler heating surface 1098 sq. ft. Wheelbase 15 ft. 6 in. Weight 30·1 tons. Stephenson's link motion. Outside sandwich frame.

PLATE 31. Stephenson's 2–2–2 i.c. locomotive, (No. 130), Midland Railway, 1852

From an engraving in the *Imperial Cyclopaedia of Machinery*. Cylinders 16 in. by 22 in. Boiler heating surface 1097 sq. ft. Wheelbase 15 ft. 6 in. Outside sandwich frame.

PLATE 32. Rothwell's 4–2–4 i.c. express tank locomotive, Bristol and Exeter Railway, 1853

From an early engraving. Broad gauge double-bogie engine designed by J. Pearson. Cylinders 16½ in. by 24 in. Wheelbase 24 ft. 9 in. Weight 42 tons. 9-ft. driving wheels.

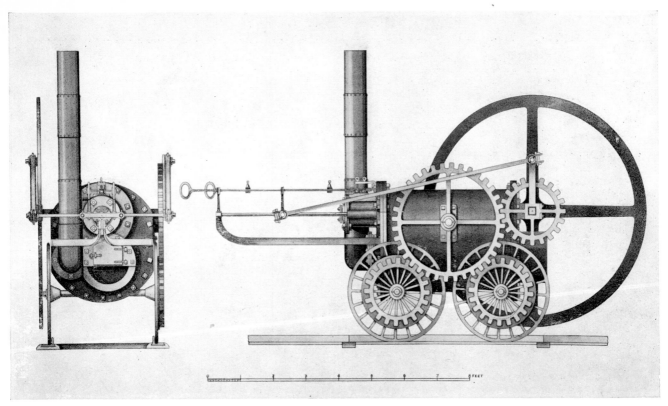

1. Trevithick's Coalbrookdale locomotive

2. Trevithick's 0–4–0 Newcastle locomotive

3. Blenkinsop's rack locomotive

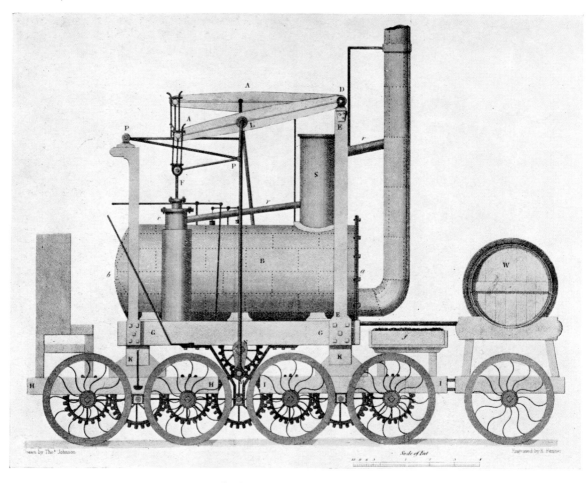

4. Hedley's 0–8–0 locomotive for Wylam

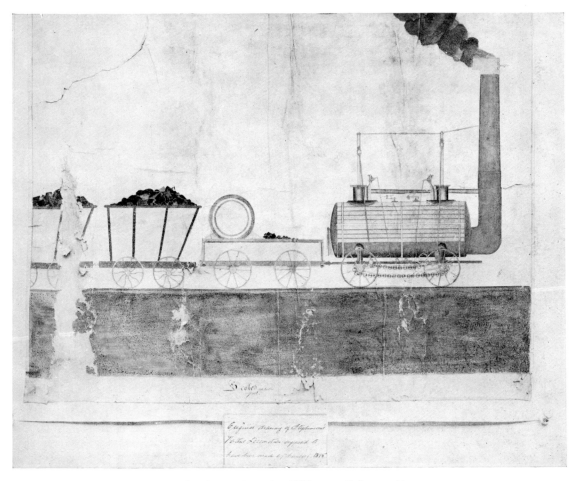

5. Stephenson's 0–4–0 Killingworth locomotive

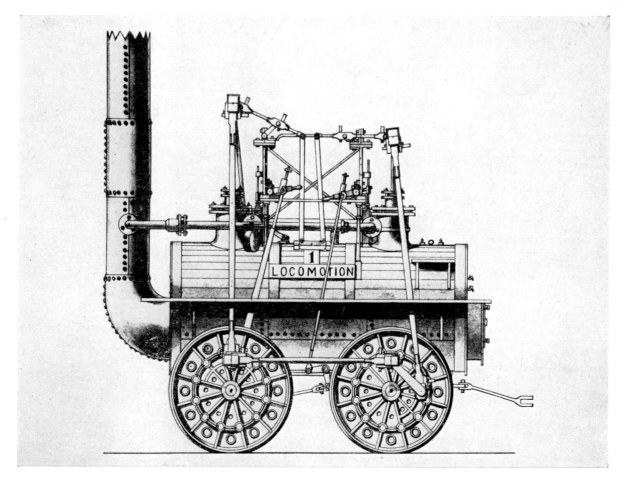

6. Stephenson's 0–4–0 *Locomotion*: Stockton and Darlington Railway

7. Hackworth's 0–6–0 *Royal George* locomotive: Stockton and Darlington Railway

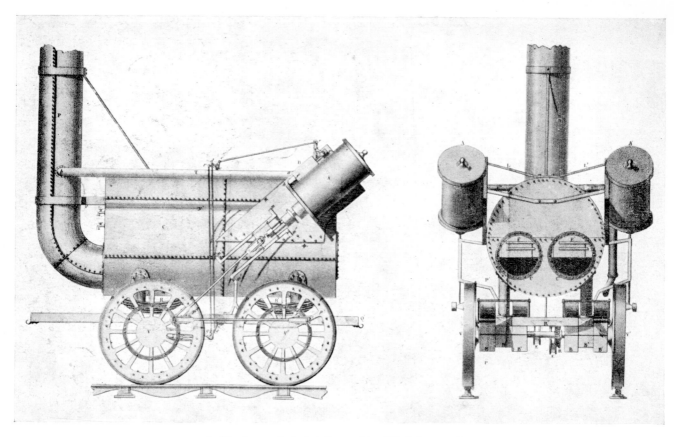

8. Stephenson's 0–4–0 *Lancashire Witch* locomotive

9. Braithwaite and Ericsson's 0–2–2 *Novelty* well-tank locomotive

10. Stephenson's 0–2–2 *Rocket* locomotive: Liverpool and Manchester Railway

THE NORTHUMBRIAN ENGINE.

11. Stephenson's 0–2–2 o.c. *Northumbrian* locomotive: Liverpool and Manchester Railway

TRAVELLING on the LIVERPOOL and MANCHESTER RAILWAY.

Lith⁴ by Baird 80ᵗʰ John Sᵗ Lpool

H Austen del

12. Stephenson's 2–2–0 i.c. *Planet* locomotive: Liverpool and Manchester Railway

13. Stephenson's 0–4–0 i.c. *George Stephenson* locomotive: Glasgow and Garnkirk Railway

14. Forrester's 2–2–0 o.c. *Vauxhall* locomotive: Dublin and Kingstown Railway

c. 1834

15. Stephenson's 0–4–0–2 i.c. goods locomotive: Stanhope and Tyne Railway

16. Tayleur's 0–6–0 i.c. locomotive: Leicester and Swannington Railway

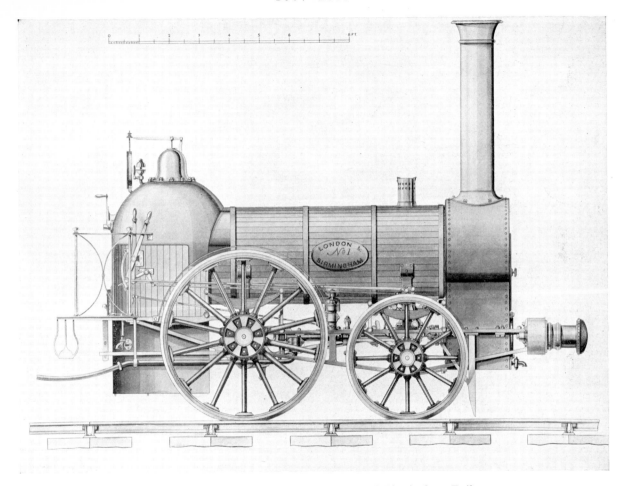

17. Bury's 2–2–0 i.c. locomotive: London and Birmingham Railway

18. Stephenson's 2–2–2 i.c. standard passenger engine

19. Norris' 4–2–0 o.c. locomotive: probably Birmingham and Gloucester Railway

20. Kitson's 0–6–0 i.c. *Hector* 'long boiler' locomotive: York and North Midland Railway

21. Stephenson's 'A' types (2–2)–2–0 o.c. 'long boiler' locomotive: London and North Western Railway (S. Division)

22. Allan's 2–2–2 o.c. *Velocipede* passenger locomotive (No. 187): London and North Western Railway (S. Division)

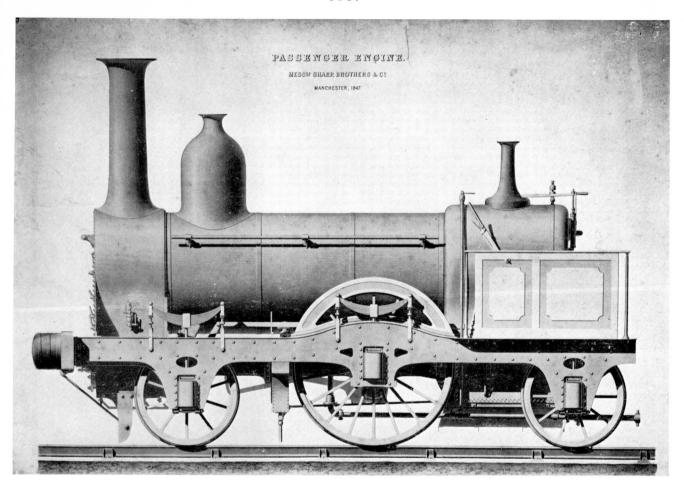

23. Sharp's 2–2–2 i.c. locomotive

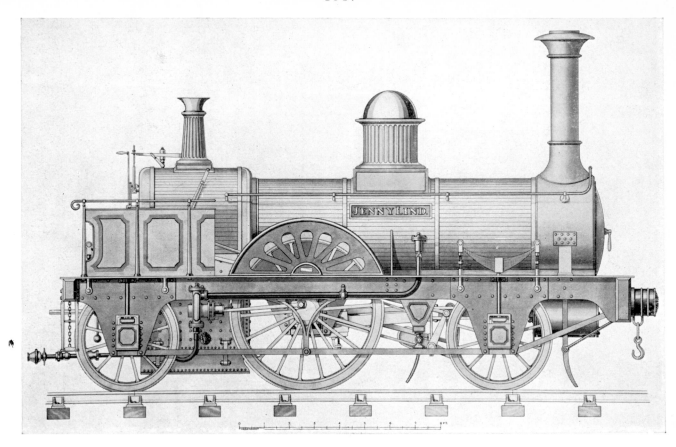

24. Wilson's 2–2–2 i.c. *Jenny Lind* locomotive

25. Gooch's 0–6–0 i.c. *Pyracmon* locomotive: Great Western Railway

26. Gooch's 2–2–2 i.c. *Queen* locomotive: Great Western Railway

27. Gooch's (2–2)–2–2 i.c. *Iron Duke* locomotive: Great Western Railway

28. Bury's (2–2–2)–2–0 o.c. *Liverpool* locomotive: London and North Western Railway

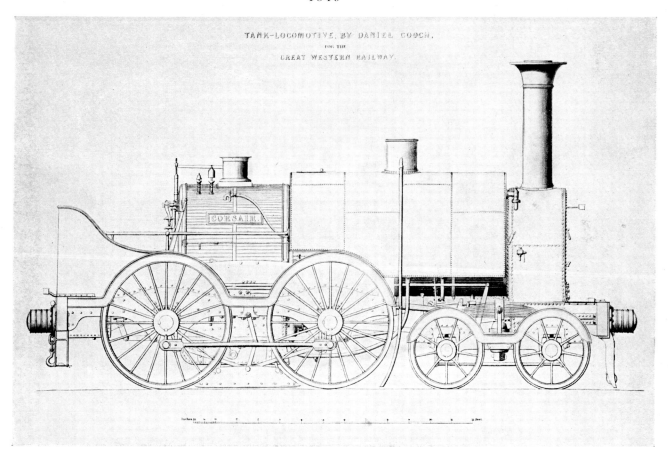

TANK-LOCOMOTIVE, BY DANIEL GOOCH,
FOR THE
GREAT WESTERN RAILWAY.

CORSAIR.

29. Gooch's 4–4–0 i.c. *Corsair* saddle tank locomotive: Great Western Railway

1852

30. Hawthorn's 2–4–0 i.c. locomotive (No. 2): Oxford, Wolverhampton and Worcester Railway

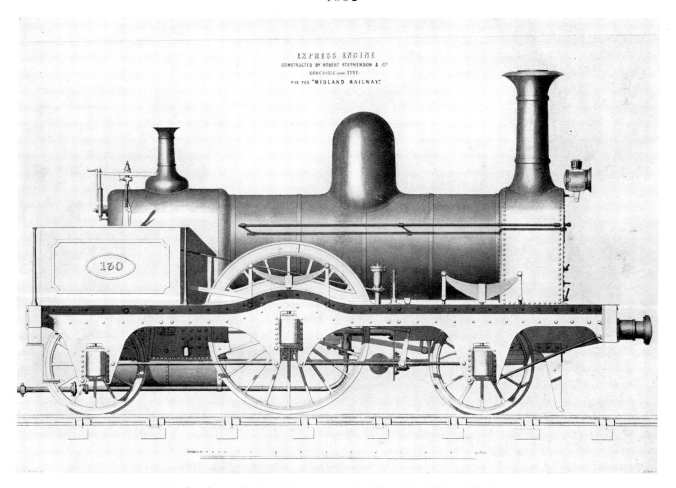

EXPRESS ENGINE
CONSTRUCTED BY ROBERT STEPHENSON & C?
NEWCASTLE UPON TYNE.
FOR THE "MIDLAND RAILWAY."

31. Stephenson's 2–2–2 i.c. locomotive (No. 130): Midland Railway

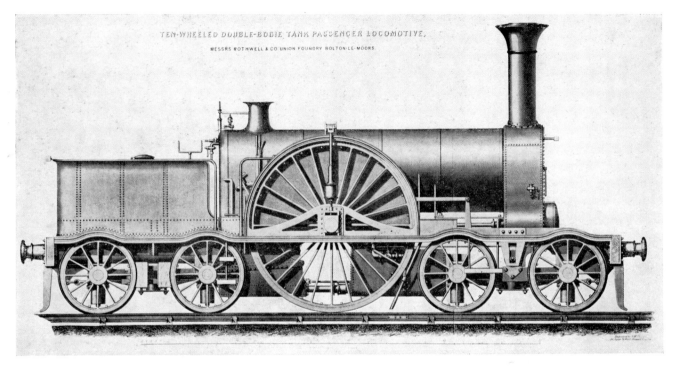

32. Rothwell's 4–2–4 i.c. express tank locomotive: Bristol and Exeter Railway